ENDORSEMENTS

'My Preemie's Journey' is a welcome companion to families navigating life with a preemie.

The NICU journey is so individual and specific to each child and his or her needs and experiences. This journey cannot be compared to any other timetable other than its own - yet it is one so worth being written.

This journal lays the foundation for milestones big and small, and provides a lasting document of single moments that weave together his or her own story.

Sarah Farnsworth - Preemie Mom and Founder of Project Hope for Babies-Central Iowa

My Preemie's Journey is the story of your baby, a beautiful way to document the trials and triumphs of each day. When your baby's NICU journey is years behind you, this beautiful keepsake will be a treasure to share with your child and demonstrate just how miraculous he or she is!

Susan Selby - Mom to Jack & Tommy and Founder of Holding Tiny Hands

This journal provides an easy-to-use tool for parents to record the day-to-day experiences of the NICU. Parents are able to follow their baby's progress and share milestones with each other and their extended family. It is an outlet for them to express their feelings and fears as they navigate the roller coaster ride of having an ill or premature newborn. My Preemie's Journey provides comfort, hope, and inspiration for those going through this life changing event.

Karen Dunn, RN - NICU Manager-retired

My Preemie's Journey is a wonderful way to help parents feel connected to their baby's NICU journey. This journal will allow them to have an outlet for their fears and emotions. As a former NICU mom and NICU nurse, I believe this journal will be an immense comfort for parents and a wonderful tracking tool for their baby's journey. It will be a wonderful way to connect with their daily emotions and possibly help other parents who are also struggling with their own NICU stay. Everyone has their own story, but at the end of the day we all have the same goals. I believe this journal will be a wonderful asset to all parents.

Shawnda Cozad, RN - NICU nurse and NICU parent

The tremendous anxiety and stress you feel when your newborn requires intensive care is difficult to put into words. Journaling is a powerful technique that can be used to combat this stress and help you to understand and share the multitude of thoughts and emotions that are ever present during your NICU stay and beyond. Tracy's journal provides a wonderful tool to help you record, reflect, and understand your NICU journey. Highly recommended.

Dan Ellsbury, MD - Neonatologist and NICU parent

MY PREEMIE'S JOURNEY

TRACY MAY

ISBN: 978-1-64085-942-5 (Paperback)
ISBN: 978-1-64085-943-2 (Hardback)
ISBN: 978-1-64085-944-9 (Ebook)

Library of Congress Control Number: 2019914428

A NOTE FROM TRACY

"You are dilated 3.5cm..."

Those are typically welcomed words for an expectant mom, but not when she is only at 19 ½ weeks gestation.

After experiencing a combined 9 ½ months in the NICU with my own micro preemie boys, I've created what I wished I would have had during that time --- a PREEMIE JOURNAL to chronicle not only your journey in the NICU but also celebrating all the milestones that continue to happen outside the NICU. Your family deserves to have a place to share your preemie journey! The moments and milestones you experience are precious, and this little book will help you hold onto each memory.

You may be surprised to find yourself holding this book. I know I was thrown for a loop with my own preemie experience. My husband and I never imagined my first pregnancy would be anything but healthy. In 2002, at 19 ½ weeks, I developed complications with my pregnancy. At my checkup, I was shocked to learn I was already dilated and was sent directly to the hospital for an emergency medical procedure and put on strict bed rest. I was also given magnesium to try and stop my contractions. That worked to an extent and on June 5, 2002, three weeks later, my son Jack was born at 22 ½ weeks gestation. His eyes were still fused shut, he weighed 1 lb. 3 oz. and was 11 ½ inches long.

I developed an infection which passed on to Jack and was likely a contributing factor in his early birth. It also led to many complications during his 196 day stay in the NICU, including brain bleeds, extended abdomen (suspected NEC) and prolonged respiratory issues.

Jack developed a retinal condition (Retinopathy of Prematurity – ROP) that can cause blindness. As a result, he endured many surgeries to keep his retinas intact. The surgeries to repair the retinal detachments were successful in his left eye, but failed in his right eye causing complete blindness. He does have functional vision in his left eye and he is currently learning Braille and is able to utilize large print material. He had a feeding tube for 10 years due to prolonged reliance on the ventilator for 4 months while his lungs matured. Jack is now 18 years old and a very happy, healthy and social kid. We continue to work on increasing his fine motor skills. He has an intellectual disability but is making steady progress in the public school system and he works hard at everything we ask him to do no matter how difficult it is.

With my second pregnancy in 2004, we knew I was at a higher risk to deliver early again. At 22 ½ weeks I started having complications and went on complete bed rest. Deja vu all over again. Our second son, Nathan, was born on May 28, 2004, at 25 ½ weeks gestation. He weighed 1 lb. 14 oz and was 14 inches long. He also developed brain bleeds and was on a ventilator, but only for 3 weeks. His stay in the NICU was much less traumatic than Jack's, but he also had his share of ups and downs. He was discharged from the NICU after 88 days and received therapy services until he was two. Nathan is now 16 years old and is on track developmentally. He is also a happy, healthy and active kid!

Jack and Nathan are our two miracle boys, and we are so blessed.

Throughout their childhood, I looked for every opportunity to get to connect with other families impacted by prematurity and became involved with the March of Dimes, serving on their Board of Directors for 10 years from 2006 to 2016. My boys would not be with us today if not for the March of Dimes and I was happy to give my time and money to an organization that was so instrumental in my children's survival. Yet I also knew that there was MORE that I could do. As I began searching for how I could serve other preemie parents, I realized that part of what I wanted MOST during my children's early days was to celebrate each new achievement, no matter how long it took my boys to reach them. I wanted a way to document this incredible journey that we were all on, and to cherish the forward momentum that my sons experienced with each passing month and year.

NICU life is tough whether for 1 day or 100 days and it is my hope that my preemie journal can provide hope for families – they can keep track of all the medical related information but it is also just a place to journal and get your feelings out on paper. Let this journal be your place of HOPE, INSPIRATION and CELEBRATION for your preemie!!

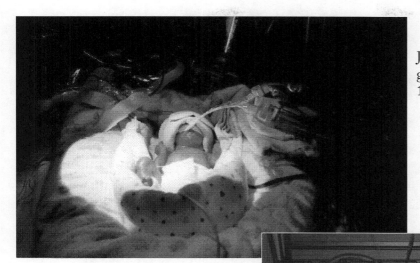

Jack born at 22 ½ weeks
gestation and weighed
1 lb. 3 oz.

Nathan born at 25 ½ weeks
gestation and weighed
1 lb. 14 oz.

The boys today - Nathan (16)
and Jack (18)

HOW TO MAKE THE MOST OF YOUR PREEMIE JOURNAL

MEDICAL INFORMATION: Your baby's oxygen level, weight, blood gas level, feedings, etc. I know that this medical information is more than just a number to you. I know that changes in the numbers can definitely set the tone for your day. So here is a safe place to record those numbers because they matter!

DAILY PLAN (tests/scans/procedures): I remember when my son was having a scan for a brain bleed and the instant anxiety it brought to me. My hope is that you are able to get what is weighing heavily on your heart onto paper to begin to alleviate some of that anxiety. In hindsight, it's been so good to look back and reflect on everything we went through even though it was a major challenge at the time.

VISITORS: Just knowing who is checking in on your child is comforting. Visitors can be great but they can also be overwhelming. Either way, I tried to remember that these visitors were a sign that I was loved and supported as a NICU mom.

TODAY AT A GLANCE: I want this section give you hope! This is space for you to capture the ups (i.e. getting to hold your baby) and downs (i.e. oxygen level spike) and overall to help you be present and just embrace the day the best you can.

HOW WAS THE DAY: There will be good days and bad days, but tracking this daily on a scale from one to five (five being the highest) will give you a big picture view and allow you to look back and be inspired by the progress your child has made.

GRATITUDE: There is no better time to start a gratitude practice. Even in spite of all the difficult moments, mindfully choosing gratitude can be life changing. If someone would have told me to write down what I was grateful for after my son was born, I would have said, "Are you kidding me, my son is fighting for his life in the NICU". Gratitude was not something I embraced early on, but I have definitely seen positive shifts in my life due to practicing daily gratitude.

Download the free 3 part NICU Survival Guide on my website to get access to an audio training where day 2 is all about the power of gratitude. www.miraclemomentsmatter.com

BLANK JOURNAL PAGE: This is space for your to get your feelings on paper and begin to share your story. You may have days where you struggle to find the words to write and days where you run out of space. Here are some journal prompts to get your mind going.

1. List 5 things that happened today that you are grateful for.
2. Write down 1 "win" you had today - it is so easy to forget all the awesome things we accomplish.
3. What is something you said to yourself today that you would not think of saying to a friend? Now replace it with something positive.

MILESTONES: At the end of the journal, you will find a "milestones" section. Your journey doesn't stop once you leave the NICU. That is why I have provided space at the end of the journal to capture the milestones once you are discharged from the NICU. Getting off oxygen, getting a feeding tube removed, walking or crawling for the first time, talking...celebrate them one by one. We are still celebrating milestones many, many years later and it has been fun to reflect back on their growth.

HOPE FOR HARD TIMES

TRACY'S ADVICE ON SURVIVING THE NICU

MY TOP 8 TIPS FOR SURVIVING THE NICU

The first few days and weeks in the NICU can be a blur. Here are some things to keep in mind as you navigate your journey in the NICU.

FRIENDSHIPS: You will make the most amazing friendships with nurses, doctors, respiratory therapists, etc. Form a bond with your child's nurses as they know your child better than anyone else. The nurses are your eyes and ears when you are away from the NICU. Talk to them, express concerns, questions, doubts, etc. They want you to be comfortable and well informed.

DOCTORS: Learn your doctors and their different personalities/tendencies as they will all do things in their own way but will ALWAYS have your child's best interest in mind.

ASK QUESTIONS: There are no wrong or dumb questions. ASK QUESTIONS!!

GRATITUDE: Gratitude is SO important and there is such power in gratitude! Your baby will have good and bad days so celebrating the little wins will help get you through the bad days. There are studies that show those who practice being grateful on a regular basis are generally happier and healthier. "Gratitude isn't the result of getting what you want, it's the result of loving what you have."

IT'S HARD: "When life's first moments are the hardest, never stop believing or lose hope!!" The NICU will test everything in your life. Your marriage, your friendships, family, etc. It's stressful, depressing, upsetting, etc. People say it gets easier... it's doesn't. NICU life is the HARDEST thing EVER!! So don't feel bad for it being an intense experience - get the support you need.

ADVOCATE: You are the best advocate for your child. Do not be afraid to speak up if something doesn't feel right.

ACCEPT YOUR JOURNEY: Comparison is the thief of joy - don't compare your baby to other babies.

PATIENCE: Patience - your baby will do things on their own timetable.

3 THINGS I LEARNED FROM OUR NICU JOURNEY

1. **BE HUMBLE**...I am a planner and going on bedrest half way through my pregnancy was not in my plan.

I was 19 ½ weeks pregnant when I was put on bedrest. That first week was all about me and humility was nowhere in sight. I hadn't prepared yet to be gone from my job for an extended period of time, I had a husband and a house to take care of and I cried every single day because this wasn't part of my plan.

After feeling sorry for myself that whole week, I began to process what had come out of the blue for me and I began to realize how selfish I was being. The next two weeks on bedrest was not about me anymore...it was about saving his life!!

> *"True humility is not thinking less of yourself, but thinking of yourself less."*
> *- C.S. Lewis -*

2. **BE PATIENT**...After he was born at 22 ½ weeks I had to learn patience very quickly. I had to learn patience waiting for his brain bleeds to resolve, patience for his reliance on the ventilator to decrease, patience waiting for him to poop for the first time, patience for him to tolerate his feedings, patience for him to be taken off the ventilator after surgery, patience waiting for doctors to determine why his abdomen was so distended. Patience, patience, patience.

No matter how quickly you want things to happen in the NICU your baby will do things on their own timetable and you have to accept that no matter how hard it is.

Today, I have to be patient as my son tries to master new life skills that are very challenging for him. It would be so easy for me to step in and do things for him but he needs and wants to be independent so I have to be patient as I watch him struggle.

3. **LEARN TO REALLY LISTEN**...In order to understand and comprehend the whole new world we were thrown into, I had to really listen. Listen to the doctors, nurses, therapists, specialists who were throwing terms at us we had never heard before.

I had to be ALL IN and PRESENT in order to fully comprehend our situation.

Today, I am a much better listener in all facets of my life because of our stay in the NICU.

3 WAYS TO NAVIGATE DIFFICULT SITUATIONS

How many times have you looked at someone else's situation and thought to yourself, I don't know who they do it, I could never do what they are doing? But you know what, you never know when you might find yourself in a difficult situation that requires a strength you never knew you had.

For me, that was my son's birth that came 4 ½ months early. There was nothing that could have prepared me for seeing my own son so small and fighting for his life.

But what I learned during his 6 ½ months in the NICU was that there are 3 things that you can do no matter the difficult situation you are facing.

1. Make acceptance a priority
Dealing with a difficult situation can be a lot like dealing with grief and the sooner you accept it, the sooner you can go from where you are and change the way you feel.

> *"Don't wait for your feelings to take action, take action and your feelings will change."*
> *- Barbara Baron -*

2. Choose to think and feel differently how you respond to the situation

> *"We cannot choose our external circumstances, but we can choose how we respond to them."*
> *- Epictetus -*

E + R = O (Event + Reaction = Outcome). The event doesn't equal the outcome but rather it is our reaction to the event that equals the outcome.

When my son was born early, I could have spent a lot of time focused on the "why" but I chose to focus my energy on staying positive. Even though he had many ups and downs, my attitude towards the situation allowed me to survive his 6 ½ month stay in the NICU.

3. Accept love and support from those around you

We are all faced with difficult situations and it's so easy to think we've got it under control and can do it on our own. After all, we are self reliant. Trust me, I know it's not easy to accept help from others but hear me when I say - people just want to help and you will be surprised how much better you will feel once you do.

If you can change your mindset around how you approach difficult situations by focusing on the 3 areas I outlined above, I promise that you will be better equipped to navigate difficult situations in the NICU and beyond!

WELCOME TO HOLLAND

by Emily Perl Kingsley
Copyright©1987 by Emily Perl Kingsley.
Reprinted by permission of the author.

I am often asked to describe the experience of raising a child with a disability - to try to help people who have not shared that unique experience to understand it, to imagine how it would feel. It's like this......

When you're going to have a baby, it's like planning a fabulous vacation trip - to Italy. You buy a bunch of guide books and make your wonderful plans. The Coliseum. The Michelangelo David. The gondolas in Venice. You may learn some handy phrases in Italian. It's all very exciting.

After months of eager anticipation, the day finally arrives. You pack your bags and off you go. Several hours later, the plane lands. The flight attendant comes in and says, "Welcome to Holland."

"Holland?!?" you say. "What do you mean Holland?? I signed up for Italy! I'm supposed to be in Italy. All my life I've dreamed of going to Italy."

But there's been a change in the flight plan. They've landed in Holland and there you must stay.

The important thing is that they haven't taken you to a horrible, disgusting, filthy place, full of pestilence, famine and disease. It's just a different place.

So you must go out and buy new guide books. And you must learn a whole new language. And you will meet a whole new group of people you would never have met.

It's just a different place. It's slower-paced than Italy, less flashy than Italy. But after you've been there for a while and you catch your breath, you look around.... and you begin to notice that Holland has windmills....and Holland has tulips. Holland even has Rembrandts.

But everyone you know is busy coming and going from Italy... and they're all bragging about what a wonderful time they had there. And for the rest of your life, you will say "Yes, that's where I was supposed to go. That's what I had planned."

And the pain of that will never, ever, ever, ever go away... because the loss of that dream is a very very significant loss.

But... if you spend your life mourning the fact that you didn't get to Italy, you may never be free to enjoy the very special, the very lovely things ... about Holland.

Years ago I attended a March of Dimes event where the Welcome to Holland essay by Emily Perl Kingsley was being read out loud. I couldn't stop the tears from flowing as I realized just how poignant the words were. In that moment everything changed for me.

I came to realize that...

> *"Happiness is letting go what you think your life is supposed to look like*
> *and celebrating it for everything that it is."*
> *– Mandy Hale –*

Can you relate?

When you are a preemie mom it is so easy to feel robbed of the opportunity to carry a baby to term and bond with your baby after giving birth. There are so many things that preemie moms don't get to experience and we find ourselves mourning all of the things that we are missing out on. But if you *switch the lens that you are looking through, you just may be surprised what you see!!"*

3 IMPORTANT STEPS TO OVERCOME PITFALLS OF COMPARISON

The day started out like any other "first day of school" morning. Rushing around to get ready so I could take the same photos of them on the front porch that I had taken since the first day of Kindergarten. Yes! I had made it through another first day of school with smiles as I watched their buses drive away.

With a full heart, I checked my phone one last time before getting ready for work and there on social media was a barrage of pictures that my friends had posted of their sophomore's in front of their cars. It hit me like a ton of bricks…the tears started rolling. My sophomore, Jack, does not have a car nor would he be driving himself to school. I was sad and I felt sad for him too.

I let that sadness consume my entire day. Any mention of school triggered another wave of tears.

Comparison: a seemingly harmless word. If we are not careful this harmless word can lead to major disappointment and discontent.

Believe me, I know all too well the feelings that accompany comparison. I had allowed comparison to invade my mind.

You see, I have a son who has an intellectual disability as well as a visual impairment. The reality is he will probably never drive. That's tough for a kid in high school when all of his friends are driving and he has to take the bus to school. I know it bothers him even though he seems to rebound pretty quickly and not let it get him down for too long. I could learn a lot from him. I wasn't able to respond quite so quickly and the sad thing is that I didn't see it coming.

How many times have we compared ourselves to someone's hairstyle, wardrobe, well manicured yard, holiday decorations, cooking, kids, etc.? It's human nature right? How does it make you feel? My guess is that is causes stress, anxiety, frustration and countless other negative emotions.

Comparison is the thief of joy and adds no value to your life. It can rob you of happiness and self confidence and create a distraction in your life.

Identifying the triggers that accompany comparison and following the steps below can help you overcome the pitfalls of comparison.

1. Practice daily gratitude and soon enough you will recognize the amazing things you already have.

2. Focus on developing an abundance mindset by spending time reflecting on the positives rather than negatives.

3. Instead of comparing to someone else, compare yourself to yourself and strive to be the best possible version of you!

> *"Everything in life is easier when you don't concern yourself*
> *with what everybody else is doing"*
> *- Author Unknown -*

ONE NICU NURSE

As I sat down to write a speech for an upcoming event to raise money for the Stead Family Children's Hospital in Iowa City...my entire story focused on thanking ONE nurse.

One nurse who had a life changing impact on me.

One nurse who was only with us for a few days!

--And I realized I had never taken the time to really thank her (until now).

Have you ever found yourself telling others how great you think someone is, and then you realize you've forgotten to tell them?

I want to walk you through three simple steps to share your gratitude with someone special in your life. I know it will make a huge difference for that person but also for you! (Research shows that expressing deep gratitude literally boosts your level of happiness).

But first Myrna.

When I first met Myrna, I was a wreck.

My son Jack was discharged from our local NICU to be transported to the NICU in Iowa City for an eye ultrasound. He had developed severe ROP (Retinopathy of Prematurity) and the ultrasound would confirm the level of retinal detachment present in each eye.

As you can imagine, my husband and I were very anxious leading up to the test. I'm sure this was very evident the first time we met Myrna, the first nurse we met in Iowa City. She went out of her way to make us feel welcome and it didn't take long before we knew that Jack was in very good hands. As a preemie mom, you know that feeling when someone new takes over your child's care which puts you on guard and a whole range of emotions flood your body.

We basically had two days to settle in before the ultrasound. We stayed at the Ronald McDonald house in Iowa City and spent most of the time at the hospital with Jack.

After the ultrasound confirmed his retinas were in need of repair we headed to Chicago. After Jack was loaded up into the incubator for his flight to Chicago we said good-bye to Myrna for the last time.

It would be years before I would think about her again.

After one of his many eye surgeries, Jack's eye pressure was elevated so we were sent to see a Glaucoma specialist in Iowa City. I called that NICU to see if Myrna was still working there as I wanted to sit down and tell her how much she meant to our family, but I had missed that opportunity. As they told me she had just recently retired, my heart sank.

I know first hand the importance of the people that have made a difference in your life and not just recognizing it but actually telling them. It's what inspired me to write this blog post.

If I had the chance to sit down with Myrna right now this is what I'd say, "You knew the severity of the situation and you did everything in your power to make us feel at home. You gave us space when we needed it but also provided a listening ear when we wanted to talk. Your calm demeanor brought about a sense of peace during a tense couple of days and saying thank you doesn't begin to convey our gratitude for all you did for us Myrna!!

Don't wait for that perfect opportunity to tell someone what they mean to you...do it right now!!

Follow these 3 steps:

STEP 1. Identify someone that has made a difference for you

STEP 2. Decide how you want to thank them because research shows that when we express our gratitude, it not only has the possibility of making a big difference for them but it also changes our own happiness level

STEP 3. Write a letter, pick up the phone or do a public post like I did and see if you can get the person to read it

You will be glad you did!!!

3 TIPS TO KNOCKING IT OUT OF THE PARK

This is the story of Jack's 10 year baseball career that I never thought would be possible.

When my boys were little I dreamed of them playing baseball. After all, little boys in baseball uniforms are adorable!! This proved challenging for Jack because of his visual impairment and intellectual disability. Organized sports weren't really an option for him so I was crushed when I realized he wouldn't have the experience that I had dreamed of him having.

When Jack turned 7, something happened that shifted everything for our family. We heard about a new adaptive baseball park that was being built right in our city. The Miracle League was built to give every child the opportunity to play baseball and we signed Jack for that first fall season. The field is made of rubber and can accommodate walkers, wheelchairs, strollers, etc. Miracle League was exactly what we were looking for!!!

Jack played on the Yankees team and we spent 8 weeks in the spring and 8 weeks in the fall cheering him on!! Given his visual impairment, it was difficult for him to be able to track the ball whether he was in the field or batting. For the first few years, most everyone on his team had to use the batting T and there were also kiddos who had to use a walker.

As the kids got older and more experienced, one by one they each found their groove and were able to hit on their own (sometimes it took 20 pitches but they did it). The kids with walkers got stronger and were eventually able to navigate the bases on their own. The transformation was incredible!!

What an incredible opportunity my son was given!! After playing for 10 years, he started to grow tired of playing baseball every Saturday. Finally one weekend he just didn't want to go and told me he wanted to retire from Miracle League.

He told me he just wanted to be done. Deep down I really wanted him to play one more year until he graduated from high school. So I had a decision to make. Do I listen to what he wants or do I encourage him play one more year?

As I reflected, I realized 3 things that I needed to do:

EMBRACE. I was holding on to what I wanted for him rather than embracing the next chapter in his journey. When we have fragile children, it's so hard to let go of being "mama bear" (a title I am proud to wear) but it's also having the courage and the confidence to know when it's time to trust the unknown even though it's difficult.

EMPOWER. Instead of dwelling on what Jack didn't want to do I needed to empower him to identify new opportunities and TOGETHER we will find that next opportunity that excites him the way Miracle League once did.

ENCOURAGE. Encouragement has so many benefits. Jack is definitely motivated by encouragement and it is important that he knows we believe in him. Encouragement also helps boost self-confidence and provides hope. Jack's decisions won't always be the right ones but knowing we support him will allow him to not shy away from challenging situations.

Focusing on these 3 actions has allowed me to really embrace his retirement from baseball. In the end, it was his decision to make. He is so proud of his great 10 year Miracle League career and so are we!!

WILL MY MARRIAGE SURVIVE?

"Odds are slim that your marriage will survive having a child in the NICU." ~ NICU nurse

WOW, I could not believe what I had just heard!

As if watching our child fight for his life isn't enough stress and worry for a lifetime, but now I had to worry about my marriage falling apart.

But deep down I knew.

I knew that my husband and I had worked hard to build a strong foundation for the first 6 years of our marriage and we weren't ready to let this tear us apart.

My guess is that you too have overcome challenges in your life that brought you to where you're at today--you survived them and they made you stronger.

--but I'll be honest and say my NICU journey was my toughest challenge yet.

Challenge #1: TIME. The first few months our son was in the NICU, that often meant that the only time we saw each other was in passing at the hospital when my husband would join us at the hospital after work or the few minutes after I got home in the evenings before bed.

Challenge #2: DIFFERENCE IN PROCESSING. It took time, but I also learned to respect that he and I processed through our emotions very differently and at different times. I learned not to push and realized that he would open up when he was ready.

Challenge #3: BALANCING ROLES. I had to balance the role of mother and wife— NICU moms face a unique challenge of feeling the need to "pick". As time went on and our son got more stable, we would take a few hours on a weekend to go for a walk or watch a movie together. I will admit that there were pangs of guilt that I should be at the NICU every waking hour I could, but I soon came to realize that he was in very capable hands in the NICU and that it was okay that I wasn't there 12 hours a day. I had someone at home that needed my attention just as much as my son did.

My husband and I didn't do date nights and we still don't, but it has always been a priority for us to spend quality time together. Sometimes it's a walk around the neighborhood, watching a favorite tv show or a little mini vacation when schedules allow.

My marriage DID survive the NICU not once but twice and despite all the challenges we have had to navigate in our 24 years together, we are still going STRONG!

INCREDIBLE STRENGTH

"You never know how strong you are, until being strong is the only choice you have."
~ Bob Marley

You already know that I'm the parent of a micro-preemie.

And for me, that's meant that I've had to rely on some unique strengths I never even knew I had before my son was born.

You see, my first pregnancy didn't exactly go as planned and my life was forever changed when my son was born 4 ½ months early. Nothing could have prepared me for the first time I would lay eyes on him. SO tiny...1 lb. 3 ozs...with translucent skin and only his tiny chin visible beneath the oversized hat and fabric goggles that covered his eyes given to him as safety measures by the hospital. Wires and tubes protruding from his body.

Shortly after my son was born, a NICU nurse informed me that odds were slim that my marriage would survive having a child in the NICU.

A problem with my marriage wasn't even on my radar. Until she mentioned the stats for marriage survival and I checked to find out that she was, in fact, correct.

So with only a 5% chance of my son surviving, I also apparently had to worry about my marriage crumbling.

Sepsis, IVH, NEC, ROP became part of our everyday vernacular. These were terms that I had never heard before and if I'm being honest, I didn't care to know what they meant. Each day brought about a new worry. The 6 ½ months we spent in the NICU brought on stress, anxiety, overwhelm and a sinking feeling of loss of control.

Despite many challenges, I was determined to stay strong for my family and channel as much positive energy as I could whenever possible.

How do you do that when the odds are stacked against you? How do you stay positive when doctors are delivering devastating news?

You have a choice.

You can choose to live your life in despair, feeling like everything is happening TO you and you're just in a constant state of reaction.

OR

You can realize that you have strengths and gifts that you may not have needed to tap into before. And now is the time to access those strengths and gifts. You can use this new challenge as an opportunity to grow, to become better for yourself and for everyone around you. AND you can find a new appreciation for the strengths of those who love and care for you. You can allow yourself to ask for the support and help that you need.

When the odds seemed stacked against you, what will you choose?

You can't always control your circumstances, but you always have control over how you react to them.

Know your strengths, leverage the strengths of those around you and most importantly... remember that no matter what challenge you're facing, as long as you're still breathing, you've got a big purpose to fulfill.

Drawing on your inner strength and choosing to persevere in hard times is the gift YOU can give to yourself and to that little one who's now depending on you.

YOUR STORY MATTERS

START SHARING IT NOW

Our Journey

Day 1

Our Journey   Day │ 1

Date _____ Nurse(s)/Doctor(s) _____

Gestational age _____ Weight/height _____

Oxygen needs _____ Apnea/brady spells _____

Feeding volume _____ Blood gas _____

Daily plan (tests/scans/procedures)

```



```

Vistors: _____
_____

Today at a glance/milestones

How was the day
1   2   3   4   5   (circle one)

```



```

Today I am GRATEFUL for: _____
_____
_____

Our Journey

Day **2**

Our Journey   Day   2

Date _____   Nurse(s)/Doctor(s) _____

Gestational age _____   Weight/height _____

Oxygen needs _____   Apnea/brady spells _____

Feeding volume _____   Blood gas _____

Daily plan (tests/scans/procedures)

```



```

Vistors: _____

_____

                                   How was the day
Today at a glance/milestones   1   2   3   4   5   (circle one)

```



```

Today I am GRATEFUL for: _____

_____

_____

Our Journey

Day 3

Our Journey

Day 3

Date _____   Nurse(s)/Doctor(s) _____

Gestational age _____   Weight/height _____

Oxygen needs _____   Apnea/brady spells _____

Feeding volume _____   Blood gas _____

Daily plan (tests/scans/procedures)

Vistors: _____

Today at a glance/milestones

How was the day

1   2   3   4   5   (circle one)

Today I am GRATEFUL for: _____

Our Journey

Day 4

Our Journey

Day 4

Date _____ Nurse(s)/Doctor(s) _____

Gestational age _____ Weight/height _____

Oxygen needs _____ Apnea/brady spells _____

Feeding volume _____ Blood gas _____

Daily plan (tests/scans/procedures)

```
[                                                                    ]
```

Vistors: _____

Today at a glance/milestones

How was the day

1   2   3   4   5   (circle one)

```
[                                                                    ]
```

Today I am GRATEFUL for: _____

_____

_____

Our Journey

Day 5

Our Journey   Day 5

Date _____ Nurse(s)/Doctor(s) _____

Gestational age _____ Weight/height _____

Oxygen needs _____ Apnea/brady spells _____

Feeding volume _____ Blood gas _____

Daily plan (tests/scans/procedures)

```
┌─────────────────────────────────────────────────────┐
│                                                       │
│                                                       │
│                                                       │
│                                                       │
│                                                       │
└─────────────────────────────────────────────────────┘
```

Vistors: _____

_____

Today at a glance/milestones

How was the day
1   2   3   4   5   (circle one)

```
┌─────────────────────────────────────────────────────┐
│                                                       │
│                                                       │
│                                                       │
│                                                       │
│                                                       │
└─────────────────────────────────────────────────────┘
```

Today I am GRATEFUL for: _____

_____

_____

"You never know how **STRONG** you are until being **STRONG** is your only choice."

Bob Marley

Photo/Keepsake

Our Journey

Day 6

Our Journey   Day   6

Date _____   Nurse(s)/Doctor(s) _____

Gestational age _____   Weight/height _____

Oxygen needs _____   Apnea/brady spells _____

Feeding volume _____   Blood gas _____

Daily plan (tests/scans/procedures)

```

```

Vistors: _____

_____

                                    How was the day
Today at a glance/milestones   1   2   3   4   5   (circle one)

```

```

Today I am GRATEFUL for: _____

_____

_____

Our Journey

Day 7

Our Journey

Day 7

Date _____ Nurse(s)/Doctor(s) _____

Gestational age _____ Weight/height _____

Oxygen needs _____ Apnea/brady spells _____

Feeding volume _____ Blood gas _____

Daily plan (tests/scans/procedures)

Vistors: _____

_____

How was the day

Today at a glance/milestones   1   2   3   4   5 (circle one)

Today I am GRATEFUL for: _____

_____

_____

Our Journey

Day | 8

Our Journey

Day 8

Date _____ Nurse(s)/Doctor(s) _____

Gestational age _____ Weight/height _____

Oxygen needs _____ Apnea/brady spells _____

Feeding volume _____ Blood gas _____

Daily plan (tests/scans/procedures)

Vistors: _____

Today at a glance/milestones

How was the day
1   2   3   4   5   (circle one)

Today I am GRATEFUL for: _____

Our Journey

Day 9

Our Journey

Day 9

Date _____ Nurse(s)/Doctor(s) _____

Gestational age _____ Weight/height _____

Oxygen needs _____ Apnea/brady spells _____

Feeding volume _____ Blood gas _____

Daily plan (tests/scans/procedures)

```
┌─────────────────────────────────────────────────┐
│                                                 │
│                                                 │
│                                                 │
│                                                 │
│                                                 │
└─────────────────────────────────────────────────┘
```

Vistors: _____

_____

How was the day

Today at a glance/milestones   1   2   3   4   5   (circle one)

```
┌─────────────────────────────────────────────────┐
│                                                 │
│                                                 │
│                                                 │
│                                                 │
│                                                 │
└─────────────────────────────────────────────────┘
```

Today I am GRATEFUL for: _____

_____

_____

Our Journey

Day 10

Our Journey   Day   10

Date _____   Nurse(s)/Doctor(s) _____

Gestational age _____   Weight/height _____

Oxygen needs _____   Apnea/brady spells _____

Feeding volume _____   Blood gas _____

Daily plan (tests/scans/procedures)

```
┌─────────────────────────────────────────────┐
│                                             │
│                                             │
│                                             │
│                                             │
│                                             │
│                                             │
└─────────────────────────────────────────────┘
```

Vistors: _____

_____

Today at a glance/milestones

How was the day

1   2   3   4   5   (circle one)

```
┌─────────────────────────────────────────────┐
│                                             │
│                                             │
│                                             │
│                                             │
│                                             │
│                                             │
└─────────────────────────────────────────────┘
```

Today I am GRATEFUL for: _____

_____

_____

"Always remember, you are
BRAVER
than you believe,
STRONGER
than you seem and
SMARTER
than you think."

A. A. Milne

Photo/Keepsake

Our Journey

Day **11**

Our Journey

Day 11

Date _____ Nurse(s)/Doctor(s) _____

Gestational age _____ Weight/height _____

Oxygen needs _____ Apnea/brady spells _____

Feeding volume _____ Blood gas _____

Daily plan (tests/scans/procedures)

[ ]

Vistors: _____

Today at a glance/milestones

How was the day
1   2   3   4   5   (circle one)

[ ]

Today I am GRATEFUL for: _____

_____

_____

Our Journey

Day 12

Our Journey

Day 12

Date _____ Nurse(s)/Doctor(s) _____

Gestational age _____ Weight/height _____

Oxygen needs _____ Apnea/brady spells _____

Feeding volume _____ Blood gas _____

Daily plan (tests/scans/procedures)

```
```

Vistors: _____

Today at a glance/milestones

How was the day
1   2   3   4   5   (circle one)

```
```

Today I am GRATEFUL for: _____

_____

_____

Our Journey

Day 13

Our Journey   Day   13

Date _____   Nurse(s)/Doctor(s) _____

Gestational age _____   Weight/height _____

Oxygen needs _____   Apnea/brady spells _____

Feeding volume _____   Blood gas _____

Daily plan (tests/scans/procedures)

```
┌─────────────────────────────────────────────┐
│                                             │
│                                             │
│                                             │
│                                             │
│                                             │
└─────────────────────────────────────────────┘
```

Vistors: _____

_____

                                    How was the day
Today at a glance/milestones   1   2   3   4   5   (circle one)

```
┌─────────────────────────────────────────────┐
│                                             │
│                                             │
│                                             │
│                                             │
│                                             │
└─────────────────────────────────────────────┘
```

Today I am GRATEFUL for: _____

_____

_____

Our Journey

Day 14

Our Journey   Day   14

Date _____   Nurse(s)/Doctor(s) _____

Gestational age _____   Weight/height _____

Oxygen needs _____   Apnea/brady spells _____

Feeding volume _____   Blood gas _____

Daily plan (tests/scans/procedures)

_____

Vistors: _____

Today at a glance/milestones

How was the day

1   2   3   4   5   (circle one)

_____

Today I am GRATEFUL for: _____

_____

_____

Our Journey

Day 15

Our Journey

Day | 15

Date _____ Nurse(s)/Doctor(s) _____

Gestational age _____ Weight/height _____

Oxygen needs _____ Apnea/brady spells _____

Feeding volume _____ Blood gas _____

Daily plan (tests/scans/procedures)

```



```

Vistors: _____

_____

How was the day

Today at a glance/milestones   1   2   3   4   5   (circle one)

```



```

Today I am GRATEFUL for: _____

_____

_____

"Nothing is impossible,
the word itself says,

'I'M POSSIBLE!'"

Audrey Hepburn

Photo/Keepsake

Our Journey

Day | 16

Our Journey   Day   16

Date _____ Nurse(s)/Doctor(s) _____

Gestational age _____ Weight/height _____

Oxygen needs _____ Apnea/brady spells _____

Feeding volume _____ Blood gas _____

Daily plan (tests/scans/procedures)

```
┌─────────────────────────────────────────────┐
│                                             │
│                                             │
│                                             │
│                                             │
│                                             │
└─────────────────────────────────────────────┘
```

Vistors: _____

_____

How was the day

Today at a glance/milestones   1   2   3   4   5   (circle one)

```
┌─────────────────────────────────────────────┐
│                                             │
│                                             │
│                                             │
│                                             │
│                                             │
└─────────────────────────────────────────────┘
```

Today I am GRATEFUL for: _____

_____

_____

Our Journey

Day 17

Our Journey

Day 17

Date _____ Nurse(s)/Doctor(s) _____

Gestational age _____ Weight/height _____

Oxygen needs _____ Apnea/brady spells _____

Feeding volume _____ Blood gas _____

Daily plan (tests/scans/procedures)

```
┌─────────────────────────────────────────────────┐
│                                                   │
│                                                   │
│                                                   │
│                                                   │
│                                                   │
└─────────────────────────────────────────────────┘
```

Vistors: _____

_____

How was the day

Today at a glance/milestones   1   2   3   4   5   (circle one)

```
┌─────────────────────────────────────────────────┐
│                                                   │
│                                                   │
│                                                   │
│                                                   │
└─────────────────────────────────────────────────┘
```

Today I am GRATEFUL for: _____

_____

_____

Our Journey

Day | **18**

Our Journey

Day 18

Date _____ Nurse(s)/Doctor(s) _____

Gestational age _____ Weight/height _____

Oxygen needs _____ Apnea/brady spells _____

Feeding volume _____ Blood gas _____

Daily plan (tests/scans/procedures)

Vistors: _____

Today at a glance/milestones

How was the day
1   2   3   4   5   (circle one)

Today I am GRATEFUL for: _____

Our Journey

Day | **19**

Our Journey   Day 19

Date _____   Nurse(s)/Doctor(s) _____

Gestational age _____   Weight/height _____

Oxygen needs _____   Apnea/brady spells _____

Feeding volume _____   Blood gas _____

Daily plan (tests/scans/procedures)

[ ]

Vistors: _____

_____

Today at a glance/milestones

How was the day

1   2   3   4   5   (circle one)

[ ]

Today I am GRATEFUL for: _____

_____

_____

Our Journey

Day 20

Our Journey

Day | 20

Date _____ Nurse(s)/Doctor(s) _____

Gestational age _____ Weight/height _____

Oxygen needs _____ Apnea/brady spells _____

Feeding volume _____ Blood gas _____

Daily plan (tests/scans/procedures)

```



```

Vistors: _____

How was the day

Today at a glance/milestones   1   2   3   4   5   (circle one)

```



```

Today I am GRATEFUL for: _____

_____

_____

"GOD made me
so that you can see
SMALL
things are
STRONG
too."

Barbara Brown

Photo/Keepsake

Our Journey

Day 21

Our Journey   Day 21

Date _____   Nurse(s)/Doctor(s) _____

Gestational age _____   Weight/height _____

Oxygen needs _____   Apnea/brady spells _____

Feeding volume _____   Blood gas _____

Daily plan (tests/scans/procedures)

Vistors: _____

How was the day

Today at a glance/milestones   1   2   3   4   5   (circle one)

Today I am GRATEFUL for: _____

_____

_____

Our Journey

Day 22

Our Journey   Day   22

Date _____ Nurse(s)/Doctor(s) _____

Gestational age _____ Weight/height _____

Oxygen needs _____ Apnea/brady spells _____

Feeding volume _____ Blood gas _____

Daily plan (tests/scans/procedures)

```



```

Vistors: _____

_____

How was the day

Today at a glance/milestones   1   2   3   4   5   (circle one)

```



```

Today I am GRATEFUL for: _____

_____

_____

Our Journey

Day | **23**

Our Journey

Day 23

Date _____ Nurse(s)/Doctor(s) _____

Gestational age _____ Weight/height _____

Oxygen needs _____ Apnea/brady spells _____

Feeding volume _____ Blood gas _____

Daily plan (tests/scans/procedures)

```
┌─────────────────────────────────────────────┐
│                                               │
│                                               │
│                                               │
│                                               │
│                                               │
└─────────────────────────────────────────────┘
```

Vistors: _____

_____

How was the day

Today at a glance/milestones   1   2   3   4   5   (circle one)

```
┌─────────────────────────────────────────────┐
│                                               │
│                                               │
│                                               │
│                                               │
└─────────────────────────────────────────────┘
```

Today I am GRATEFUL for: _____

_____

_____

Our Journey

Day **24**

Our Journey   Day   24

Date _____   Nurse(s)/Doctor(s) _____

Gestational age _____   Weight/height _____

Oxygen needs _____   Apnea/brady spells _____

Feeding volume _____   Blood gas _____

Daily plan (tests/scans/procedures)

```
```

Vistors: _____

Today at a glance/milestones

How was the day

1   2   3   4   5   (circle one)

```
```

Today I am GRATEFUL for: _____

_____

_____

Our Journey

Day 25

Our Journey

Day 25

Date _____ Nurse(s)/Doctor(s) _____

Gestational age _____ Weight/height _____

Oxygen needs _____ Apnea/brady spells _____

Feeding volume _____ Blood gas _____

Daily plan (tests/scans/procedures)

[empty box]

Vistors: _____

How was the day

Today at a glance/milestones   1   2   3   4   5   (circle one)

[empty box]

Today I am GRATEFUL for: _____

_____

_____

"Anyone can give up,
it's the easiest thing in
the world to do. But to

HOLD

it together when everyone
else would understand
if you fell apart, that's

TRUE STRENGTH."

Author unknown

Photo/Keepsake

Our Journey

Day **26**

Our Journey

Day 26

Date _____ Nurse(s)/Doctor(s) _____

Gestational age _____ Weight/height _____

Oxygen needs _____ Apnea/brady spells _____

Feeding volume _____ Blood gas _____

Daily plan (tests/scans/procedures)

_____

Vistors: _____

_____

How was the day

Today at a glance/milestones   1   2   3   4   5   (circle one)

_____

Today I am GRATEFUL for: _____

_____

_____

Our Journey

Day 27

Our Journey

Day 27

Date _____ Nurse(s)/Doctor(s) _____

Gestational age _____ Weight/height _____

Oxygen needs _____ Apnea/brady spells _____

Feeding volume _____ Blood gas _____

Daily plan (tests/scans/procedures)

Vistors: _____

_____

How was the day

Today at a glance/milestones   1   2   3   4   5   (circle one)

Today I am GRATEFUL for: _____

_____

_____

Our Journey

Day | 28

Our Journey   Day   28

Date _____   Nurse(s)/Doctor(s) _____

Gestational age _____   Weight/height _____

Oxygen needs _____   Apnea/brady spells _____

Feeding volume _____   Blood gas _____

Daily plan (tests/scans/procedures)

Vistors: _____

_____

How was the day

Today at a glance/milestones   1   2   3   4   5   (circle one)

Today I am GRATEFUL for: _____

_____

_____

Our Journey

Day 29

Our Journey

Day 29

Date _____ Nurse(s)/Doctor(s) _____

Gestational age _____ Weight/height _____

Oxygen needs _____ Apnea/brady spells _____

Feeding volume _____ Blood gas _____

Daily plan (tests/scans/procedures)

```
┌─────────────────────────────────────────────────┐
│                                                   │
│                                                   │
│                                                   │
│                                                   │
│                                                   │
└─────────────────────────────────────────────────┘
```

Vistors: _____

How was the day

Today at a glance/milestones   1   2   3   4   5   (circle one)

```
┌─────────────────────────────────────────────────┐
│                                                   │
│                                                   │
│                                                   │
│                                                   │
│                                                   │
└─────────────────────────────────────────────────┘
```

Today I am GRATEFUL for: _____

_____

_____

Our Journey

Day 30

_____
_____
_____
_____
_____
_____
_____
_____
_____
_____
_____
_____
_____
_____
_____
_____
_____
_____
_____
_____
_____
_____
_____
_____

Our Journey

Day | 30

Date _____ Nurse(s)/Doctor(s) _____

Gestational age _____ Weight/height _____

Oxygen needs _____ Apnea/brady spells _____

Feeding volume _____ Blood gas _____

Daily plan (tests/scans/procedures)

_____

Vistors: _____

Today at a glance/milestones

How was the day
1   2   3   4   5   (circle one)

_____

Today I am GRATEFUL for: _____

_____

"A **HERO** isn't always big and strong and is simply one who has the **STRENGTH** and **COURAGE** to overcome overwhelming circumstances."

Author unknown

Photo/Keepsake

Our Journey

Day | 31

Our Journey   Day | 31

Date _____ Nurse(s)/Doctor(s) _____

Gestational age _____ Weight/height _____

Oxygen needs _____ Apnea/brady spells _____

Feeding volume _____ Blood gas _____

Daily plan (tests/scans/procedures)

```



```

Vistors: _____

_____

Today at a glance/milestones

How was the day
1   2   3   4   5   (circle one)

```



```

Today I am GRATEFUL for: _____

_____

_____

Our Journey

Day | 32

Our Journey   Day   32

Date _____   Nurse(s)/Doctor(s) _____

Gestational age _____   Weight/height _____

Oxygen needs _____   Apnea/brady spells _____

Feeding volume _____   Blood gas _____

Daily plan (tests/scans/procedures)

```




```

Vistors: _____

_____

How was the day

Today at a glance/milestones   1   2   3   4   5   (circle one)

```




```

Today I am GRATEFUL for: _____

_____

_____

Our Journey

Day 33

Our Journey   Day   33

Date _____   Nurse(s)/Doctor(s) _____

Gestational age _____   Weight/height _____

Oxygen needs _____   Apnea/brady spells _____

Feeding volume _____   Blood gas _____

Daily plan (tests/scans/procedures)

```



```

Vistors: _____

Today at a glance/milestones

How was the day
1   2   3   4   5   (circle one)

```



```

Today I am GRATEFUL for: _____

_____

_____

Our Journey

Day | 34

Our Journey

Day 34

Date _____ Nurse(s)/Doctor(s) _____

Gestational age _____ Weight/height _____

Oxygen needs _____ Apnea/brady spells _____

Feeding volume _____ Blood gas _____

Daily plan (tests/scans/procedures)

Vistors: _____

Today at a glance/milestones

How was the day

1   2   3   4   5   (circle one)

Today I am GRATEFUL for: _____

Our Journey

Day 35

Our Journey

Day | 35

Date _____ Nurse(s)/Doctor(s) _____

Gestational age _____ Weight/height _____

Oxygen needs _____ Apnea/brady spells _____

Feeding volume _____ Blood gas _____

Daily plan (tests/scans/procedures)

```
[blank box]
```

Vistors: _____

_____

Today at a glance/milestones

How was the day
1   2   3   4   5   (circle one)

```
[blank box]
```

Today I am GRATEFUL for: _____

_____

_____

"Don't let the fear steal your joy. Even in the darkest of times —

FIND JOY. "

Author unknown

Photo/Keepsake

Our Journey

Day 36

Our Journey   Day 36

Date _____   Nurse(s)/Doctor(s) _____

Gestational age _____   Weight/height _____

Oxygen needs _____   Apnea/brady spells _____

Feeding volume _____   Blood gas _____

Daily plan (tests/scans/procedures)

```
┌─────────────────────────────────────────────┐
│                                             │
│                                             │
│                                             │
│                                             │
│                                             │
│                                             │
└─────────────────────────────────────────────┘
```

Vistors: _____

_____

How was the day

Today at a glance/milestones   1   2   3   4   5   (circle one)

```
┌─────────────────────────────────────────────┐
│                                             │
│                                             │
│                                             │
│                                             │
│                                             │
│                                             │
└─────────────────────────────────────────────┘
```

Today I am GRATEFUL for: _____

_____

_____

Our Journey

Day | **37**

Our Journey   Day 37

Date _____   Nurse(s)/Doctor(s) _____

Gestational age _____   Weight/height _____

Oxygen needs _____   Apnea/brady spells _____

Feeding volume _____   Blood gas _____

Daily plan (tests/scans/procedures)

```
┌─────────────────────────────────────────┐
│                                           │
│                                           │
│                                           │
│                                           │
│                                           │
└─────────────────────────────────────────┘
```

Vistors: _____

How was the day

Today at a glance/milestones   1   2   3   4   5   (circle one)

```
┌─────────────────────────────────────────┐
│                                           │
│                                           │
│                                           │
│                                           │
└─────────────────────────────────────────┘
```

Today I am GRATEFUL for: _____

_____

_____

Our Journey

Day 38

Our Journey   Day   38

Date _____   Nurse(s)/Doctor(s) _____

Gestational age _____   Weight/height _____

Oxygen needs _____   Apnea/brady spells _____

Feeding volume _____   Blood gas _____

Daily plan (tests/scans/procedures)

```
┌─────────────────────────────────────────────────┐
│                                                   │
│                                                   │
│                                                   │
│                                                   │
│                                                   │
└─────────────────────────────────────────────────┘
```

Vistors: _____

_____

                                    How was the day
Today at a glance/milestones   1   2   3   4   5   (circle one)

```
┌─────────────────────────────────────────────────┐
│                                                   │
│                                                   │
│                                                   │
│                                                   │
│                                                   │
└─────────────────────────────────────────────────┘
```

Today I am GRATEFUL for: _____

_____

_____

Our Journey

Day 39

Our Journey   Day 39

Date _____   Nurse(s)/Doctor(s) _____

Gestational age _____   Weight/height _____

Oxygen needs _____   Apnea/brady spells _____

Feeding volume _____   Blood gas _____

Daily plan (tests/scans/procedures)

```
[                                                                    ]
```

Vistors: _____

_____

How was the day

Today at a glance/milestones   1   2   3   4   5   (circle one)

```
[                                                                    ]
```

Today I am GRATEFUL for: _____

_____

_____

Our Journey

Day **40**

Our Journey   Day 40

Date _____ Nurse(s)/Doctor(s) _____

Gestational age _____ Weight/height _____

Oxygen needs _____ Apnea/brady spells _____

Feeding volume _____ Blood gas _____

Daily plan (tests/scans/procedures)

```
```

Vistors: _____

_____

How was the day

Today at a glance/milestones   1   2   3   4   5   (circle one)

```
```

Today I am GRATEFUL for: _____

_____

_____

"You can do the
IMPOSSIBLE
because you've been through the
UNIMAGINABLE."

Author unknown

Photo/Keepsake

Our Journey

Day | **41**

Our Journey

Day 41

Date _____ Nurse(s)/Doctor(s) _____

Gestational age _____ Weight/height _____

Oxygen needs _____ Apnea/brady spells _____

Feeding volume _____ Blood gas _____

Daily plan (tests/scans/procedures)

```



```

Vistors: _____

_____

Today at a glance/milestones

How was the day

1 2 3 4 5 (circle one)

```



```

Today I am GRATEFUL for: _____

_____

_____

Our Journey

Day 42

Our Journey

Day | 42

Date _____ Nurse(s)/Doctor(s) _____

Gestational age _____ Weight/height _____

Oxygen needs _____ Apnea/brady spells _____

Feeding volume _____ Blood gas _____

Daily plan (tests/scans/procedures)

┌───┐
│   │
│   │
│   │
│   │
└───┘

Vistors: _____

How was the day

Today at a glance/milestones   1   2   3   4   5   (circle one)

┌───┐
│   │
│   │
│   │
│   │
└───┘

Today I am GRATEFUL for: _____

_____

_____

Our Journey

Day 43

Our Journey   Day 43

Date _____   Nurse(s)/Doctor(s) _____

Gestational age _____   Weight/height _____

Oxygen needs _____   Apnea/brady spells _____

Feeding volume _____   Blood gas _____

Daily plan (tests/scans/procedures)

```




```

Vistors: _____

                                            How was the day
Today at a glance/milestones   1   2   3   4   5   (circle one)

```




```

Today I am GRATEFUL for: _____

_____

_____

Our Journey

Day 44

Our Journey Day 44

Date _____ Nurse(s)/Doctor(s) _____

Gestational age _____ Weight/height _____

Oxygen needs _____ Apnea/brady spells _____

Feeding volume _____ Blood gas _____

Daily plan (tests/scans/procedures)

Vistors: _____

_____

Today at a glance/milestones

How was the day
1 2 3 4 5 (circle one)

Today I am GRATEFUL for: _____

_____

_____

Our Journey

Day | 45

Our Journey   Day 45

Date _____   Nurse(s)/Doctor(s) _____

Gestational age _____   Weight/height _____

Oxygen needs _____   Apnea/brady spells _____

Feeding volume _____   Blood gas _____

Daily plan (tests/scans/procedures)

```
┌────────────────────────────────────────────┐
│                                            │
│                                            │
│                                            │
│                                            │
│                                            │
│                                            │
└────────────────────────────────────────────┘
```

Vistors: _____

_____

How was the day

Today at a glance/milestones   1   2   3   4   5   (circle one)

```
┌────────────────────────────────────────────┐
│                                            │
│                                            │
│                                            │
│                                            │
│                                            │
└────────────────────────────────────────────┘
```

Today I am GRATEFUL for: _____

_____

_____

"The **BEST** and **STRONGEST** things in life come in small packages."

Author Unknown

Photo/Keepsake

Our Journey   Day   46

Our Journey   Day   46

Date _____   Nurse(s)/Doctor(s) _____

Gestational age _____   Weight/height _____

Oxygen needs _____   Apnea/brady spells _____

Feeding volume _____   Blood gas _____

Daily plan (tests/scans/procedures)

Vistors: _____
_____

Today at a glance/milestones

How was the day

1   2   3   4   5   (circle one)

Today I am GRATEFUL for: _____
_____
_____

Our Journey

Day **47**

Our Journey   Day 47

Date _____ Nurse(s)/Doctor(s) _____

Gestational age _____ Weight/height _____

Oxygen needs _____ Apnea/brady spells _____

Feeding volume _____ Blood gas _____

Daily plan (tests/scans/procedures)

```




```

Vistors: _____

_____

Today at a glance/milestones

How was the day
1   2   3   4   5   (circle one)

```




```

Today I am GRATEFUL for: _____

_____

_____

Our Journey

Day 48

Our Journey   Day   48

Date _____   Nurse(s)/Doctor(s) _____

Gestational age _____   Weight/height _____

Oxygen needs _____   Apnea/brady spells _____

Feeding volume _____   Blood gas _____

Daily plan (tests/scans/procedures)

```
┌─────────────────────────────────────────────────────────┐
│                                                         │
│                                                         │
│                                                         │
│                                                         │
│                                                         │
└─────────────────────────────────────────────────────────┘
```

Vistors: _____

_____

Today at a glance/milestones

How was the day

1   2   3   4   5   (circle one)

```
┌─────────────────────────────────────────────────────────┐
│                                                         │
│                                                         │
│                                                         │
│                                                         │
│                                                         │
└─────────────────────────────────────────────────────────┘
```

Today I am GRATEFUL for: _____

_____

_____

Our Journey

Day 49

Our Journey

Day 49

Date _____ Nurse(s)/Doctor(s) _____

Gestational age _____ Weight/height _____

Oxygen needs _____ Apnea/brady spells _____

Feeding volume _____ Blood gas _____

Daily plan (tests/scans/procedures)

Vistors: _____

How was the day

Today at a glance/milestones   1   2   3   4   5   (circle one)

Today I am GRATEFUL for: _____

Our Journey

Day 50

Our Journey

Day 50

Date _____ Nurse(s)/Doctor(s) _____

Gestational age _____ Weight/height _____

Oxygen needs _____ Apnea/brady spells _____

Feeding volume _____ Blood gas _____

Daily plan (tests/scans/procedures)

Vistors: _____

Today at a glance/milestones

How was the day

1   2   3   4   5   (circle one)

Today I am GRATEFUL for: _____

"Challenges are what make
life interesting and

OVERCOMING

them is what makes life

MEANINGFUL."

Joshua L. Marine

Photo/Keepsake

Our Journey

Day 51

Our Journey

Day 51

Date _____ Nurse(s)/Doctor(s) _____

Gestational age _____ Weight/height _____

Oxygen needs _____ Apnea/brady spells _____

Feeding volume _____ Blood gas _____

Daily plan (tests/scans/procedures)

```



```

Vistors: _____

_____

How was the day

Today at a glance/milestones   1   2   3   4   5   (circle one)

```



```

Today I am GRATEFUL for: _____

_____

_____

Our Journey

Day 52

Our Journey   Day 52

Date _____   Nurse(s)/Doctor(s) _____

Gestational age _____   Weight/height _____

Oxygen needs _____   Apnea/brady spells _____

Feeding volume _____   Blood gas _____

Daily plan (tests/scans/procedures)

```
[                                                          ]
[                                                          ]
[                                                          ]
[                                                          ]
```

Vistors: _____

_____

Today at a glance/milestones

How was the day

1   2   3   4   5   (circle one)

```
[                                                          ]
[                                                          ]
[                                                          ]
[                                                          ]
```

Today I am GRATEFUL for: _____

_____

_____

Our Journey

Day 53

Our Journey

Day 53

Date _____ Nurse(s)/Doctor(s) _____

Gestational age _____ Weight/height _____

Oxygen needs _____ Apnea/brady spells _____

Feeding volume _____ Blood gas _____

Daily plan (tests/scans/procedures)

_____

Vistors: _____

Today at a glance/milestones

How was the day

1   2   3   4   5   (circle one)

_____

Today I am GRATEFUL for: _____

Our Journey

Day 54

Our Journey

Day 54

Date _____   Nurse(s)/Doctor(s) _____

Gestational age _____   Weight/height _____

Oxygen needs _____   Apnea/brady spells _____

Feeding volume _____   Blood gas _____

Daily plan (tests/scans/procedures)

```
┌──────────────────────────────────────────┐
│                                            │
│                                            │
│                                            │
│                                            │
│                                            │
│                                            │
└──────────────────────────────────────────┘
```

Vistors: _____

_____

How was the day

Today at a glance/milestones   1 2 3 4 5 (circle one)

```
┌──────────────────────────────────────────┐
│                                            │
│                                            │
│                                            │
│                                            │
│                                            │
└──────────────────────────────────────────┘
```

Today I am GRATEFUL for: _____

_____

_____

Our Journey

Our Journey   Day   55

Date _____ Nurse(s)/Doctor(s) _____

Gestational age _____ Weight/height _____

Oxygen needs _____ Apnea/brady spells _____

Feeding volume _____ Blood gas _____

Daily plan (tests/scans/procedures)

[   ]

Vistors: _____

_____

Today at a glance/milestones

How was the day

1   2   3   4   5   (circle one)

[   ]

Today I am GRATEFUL for: _____

_____

_____

"**FAITH**
is taking the first step
even when you can't
see the whole staircase."

Dr. Martin Luther King Jr.

Photo/Keepsake

Our Journey

Day **56**

Our Journey

Day 56

Date _____ Nurse(s)/Doctor(s) _____

Gestational age _____ Weight/height _____

Oxygen needs _____ Apnea/brady spells _____

Feeding volume _____ Blood gas _____

Daily plan (tests/scans/procedures)

```
┌─────────────────────────────────────────────────────────┐
│                                                           │
│                                                           │
│                                                           │
│                                                           │
│                                                           │
└─────────────────────────────────────────────────────────┘
```

Vistors: _____
_____

Today at a glance/milestones

How was the day
1   2   3   4   5   (circle one)

```
┌─────────────────────────────────────────────────────────┐
│                                                           │
│                                                           │
│                                                           │
│                                                           │
│                                                           │
└─────────────────────────────────────────────────────────┘
```

Today I am GRATEFUL for: _____
_____
_____

Our Journey

Day | 57

Our Journey

Day 57

Date _____ Nurse(s)/Doctor(s) _____

Gestational age _____ Weight/height _____

Oxygen needs _____ Apnea/brady spells _____

Feeding volume _____ Blood gas _____

Daily plan (tests/scans/procedures)

Vistors: _____

How was the day

Today at a glance/milestones 1 2 3 4 5 (circle one)

Today I am GRATEFUL for: _____

Our Journey

Day | 58

Our Journey

Day 58

Date _____ Nurse(s)/Doctor(s) _____

Gestational age _____ Weight/height _____

Oxygen needs _____ Apnea/brady spells _____

Feeding volume _____ Blood gas _____

Daily plan (tests/scans/procedures)

```
┌─────────────────────────────────────────────┐
│                                               │
│                                               │
│                                               │
│                                               │
│                                               │
└─────────────────────────────────────────────┘
```

Vistors: _____

_____

How was the day

Today at a glance/milestones   1   2   3   4   5   (circle one)

```
┌─────────────────────────────────────────────┐
│                                               │
│                                               │
│                                               │
│                                               │
│                                               │
└─────────────────────────────────────────────┘
```

Today I am GRATEFUL for: _____

_____

_____

Our Journey

Day 59

Our Journey   Day   59

Date _____   Nurse(s)/Doctor(s) _____

Gestational age _____   Weight/height _____

Oxygen needs _____   Apnea/brady spells _____

Feeding volume _____   Blood gas _____

Daily plan (tests/scans/procedures)

```
┌─────────────────────────────────────────────────┐
│                                                   │
│                                                   │
│                                                   │
│                                                   │
│                                                   │
└─────────────────────────────────────────────────┘
```

Vistors: _____

_____

Today at a glance/milestones

How was the day

1   2   3   4   5   (circle one)

```
┌─────────────────────────────────────────────────┐
│                                                   │
│                                                   │
│                                                   │
│                                                   │
│                                                   │
└─────────────────────────────────────────────────┘
```

Today I am GRATEFUL for: _____

_____

_____

Our Journey

Day 60

Our Journey

Day 60

Date _____ Nurse(s)/Doctor(s) _____

Gestational age _____ Weight/height _____

Oxygen needs _____ Apnea/brady spells _____

Feeding volume _____ Blood gas _____

Daily plan (tests/scans/procedures)

```
                                                            
                                                            
                                                            
                                                            
                                                            
```

Vistors: _____

How was the day

Today at a glance/milestones   1   2   3   4   5   (circle one)

```
                                                            
                                                            
                                                            
                                                            
                                                            
```

Today I am GRATEFUL for: _____

_____

_____

"I may have
little feet but I make

BIG

strides everyday."

Author unknown

Photo/Keepsake

Our Journey

Day | 61

Our Journey   Day   61

Date _____   Nurse(s)/Doctor(s) _____

Gestational age _____   Weight/height _____

Oxygen needs _____   Apnea/brady spells _____

Feeding volume _____   Blood gas _____

Daily plan (tests/scans/procedures)

Vistors: _____

Today at a glance/milestones

How was the day

1   2   3   4   5   (circle one)

Today I am GRATEFUL for: _____

Our Journey

Day | 62

Our Journey

Day 62

Date _____ Nurse(s)/Doctor(s) _____

Gestational age _____ Weight/height _____

Oxygen needs _____ Apnea/brady spells _____

Feeding volume _____ Blood gas _____

Daily plan (tests/scans/procedures)

```



```

Vistors: _____

How was the day

Today at a glance/milestones   1   2   3   4   5   (circle one)

```



```

Today I am GRATEFUL for: _____

_____

_____

Our Journey

Day 63

Our Journey

Day 63

Date _____   Nurse(s)/Doctor(s) _____

Gestational age _____   Weight/height _____

Oxygen needs _____   Apnea/brady spells _____

Feeding volume _____   Blood gas _____

Daily plan (tests/scans/procedures)

Vistors: _____

How was the day

1   2   3   4   5   (circle one)

Today at a glance/milestones

Today I am GRATEFUL for: _____

Our Journey

Day 64

Our Journey

Day 64

Date _____ Nurse(s)/Doctor(s) _____

Gestational age _____ Weight/height _____

Oxygen needs _____ Apnea/brady spells _____

Feeding volume _____ Blood gas _____

Daily plan (tests/scans/procedures)

```


```

Vistors: _____

How was the day

Today at a glance/milestones   1   2   3   4   5   (circle one)

```


```

Today I am GRATEFUL for: _____

_____

_____

Our Journey

Day 65

Our Journey

Day 65

Date _____   Nurse(s)/Doctor(s) _____

Gestational age _____   Weight/height _____

Oxygen needs _____   Apnea/brady spells _____

Feeding volume _____   Blood gas _____

Daily plan (tests/scans/procedures)

_____

Vistors: _____

How was the day

Today at a glance/milestones   1   2   3   4   5   (circle one)

_____

Today I am GRATEFUL for: _____

_____

_____

"You were given this **LIFE** because you are **STRONG** enough to live it."

Robin Sharma

Photo/Keepsake

Our Journey

Day 66

Our Journey   Day   66

Date _____   Nurse(s)/Doctor(s) _____

Gestational age _____   Weight/height _____

Oxygen needs _____   Apnea/brady spells _____

Feeding volume _____   Blood gas _____

Daily plan (tests/scans/procedures)

```
┌─────────────────────────────────────────┐
│                                         │
│                                         │
│                                         │
│                                         │
│                                         │
│                                         │
│                                         │
└─────────────────────────────────────────┘
```

Vistors: _____

_____

How was the day

Today at a glance/milestones   1   2   3   4   5   (circle one)

```
┌─────────────────────────────────────────┐
│                                         │
│                                         │
│                                         │
│                                         │
│                                         │
│                                         │
└─────────────────────────────────────────┘
```

Today I am GRATEFUL for: _____

_____

_____

Our Journey

Day **67**

Our Journey   Day 67

Date _____   Nurse(s)/Doctor(s) _____

Gestational age _____   Weight/height _____

Oxygen needs _____   Apnea/brady spells _____

Feeding volume _____   Blood gas _____

Daily plan (tests/scans/procedures)

```



```

Vistors: _____

_____

Today at a glance/milestones

How was the day

1   2   3   4   5   (circle one)

```



```

Today I am GRATEFUL for: _____

_____

_____

Our Journey

Day | 68

Our Journey   Day 68

Date _____   Nurse(s)/Doctor(s) _____

Gestational age _____   Weight/height _____

Oxygen needs _____   Apnea/brady spells _____

Feeding volume _____   Blood gas _____

Daily plan (tests/scans/procedures)

```
┌─────────────────────────────────────────────────────┐
│                                                       │
│                                                       │
│                                                       │
│                                                       │
│                                                       │
│                                                       │
└─────────────────────────────────────────────────────┘
```

Vistors: _____

_____

How was the day

Today at a glance/milestones   1   2   3   4   5   (circle one)

```
┌─────────────────────────────────────────────────────┐
│                                                       │
│                                                       │
│                                                       │
│                                                       │
│                                                       │
│                                                       │
└─────────────────────────────────────────────────────┘
```

Today I am GRATEFUL for: _____

_____

_____

Our Journey

Day 69

Our Journey   Day   69

Date _____   Nurse(s)/Doctor(s) _____

Gestational age _____   Weight/height _____

Oxygen needs _____   Apnea/brady spells _____

Feeding volume _____   Blood gas _____

Daily plan (tests/scans/procedures)

Vistors: _____

Today at a glance/milestones

How was the day

1   2   3   4   5   (circle one)

Today I am GRATEFUL for: _____

Our Journey

Day | 70

Our Journey   Day 70

Date _____ Nurse(s)/Doctor(s) _____

Gestational age _____ Weight/height _____

Oxygen needs _____ Apnea/brady spells _____

Feeding volume _____ Blood gas _____

Daily plan (tests/scans/procedures)

[ ]

Vistors: _____

_____

Today at a glance/milestones

How was the day
1   2   3   4   5   (circle one)

[ ]

Today I am GRATEFUL for: _____

_____

_____

"There is no

FOOTPRINT

so **SMALL**

that it does not leave an

IMPRINT

on this world."

Author unknown

Photo/Keepsake

Our Journey

Day | 71

Our Journey   Day   71

Date _____   Nurse(s)/Doctor(s) _____

Gestational age _____   Weight/height _____

Oxygen needs _____   Apnea/brady spells _____

Feeding volume _____   Blood gas _____

Daily plan (tests/scans/procedures)

```
```

Vistors: _____

_____

How was the day

Today at a glance/milestones   1   2   3   4   5   (circle one)

```
```

Today I am GRATEFUL for: _____

_____

_____

Our Journey

Day 72

Our Journey

Day 72

Date _____ Nurse(s)/Doctor(s) _____

Gestational age _____ Weight/height _____

Oxygen needs _____ Apnea/brady spells _____

Feeding volume _____ Blood gas _____

Daily plan (tests/scans/procedures)

```



```

Vistors: _____

_____

How was the day

Today at a glance/milestones   1   2   3   4   5   (circle one)

```



```

Today I am GRATEFUL for: _____

_____

_____

Our Journey

Day 73

Our Journey

Day | 73

Date _____ Nurse(s)/Doctor(s) _____

Gestational age _____ Weight/height _____

Oxygen needs _____ Apnea/brady spells _____

Feeding volume _____ Blood gas _____

Daily plan (tests/scans/procedures)

```
```

Vistors: _____

How was the day

Today at a glance/milestones   1   2   3   4   5   (circle one)

```
```

Today I am GRATEFUL for: _____

_____

_____

Our Journey

Day 74

Our Journey   Day 74

Date _____   Nurse(s)/Doctor(s) _____

Gestational age _____   Weight/height _____

Oxygen needs _____   Apnea/brady spells _____

Feeding volume _____   Blood gas _____

Daily plan (tests/scans/procedures)

```
┌─────────────────────────────────────────┐
│                                           │
│                                           │
│                                           │
│                                           │
│                                           │
└─────────────────────────────────────────┘
```

Vistors: _____

_____

                                  How was the day
Today at a glance/milestones   1   2   3   4   5   (circle one)

```
┌─────────────────────────────────────────┐
│                                           │
│                                           │
│                                           │
│                                           │
│                                           │
└─────────────────────────────────────────┘
```

Today I am GRATEFUL for: _____

_____

_____

Our Journey

Day | 75

Our Journey

Day 75

Date _____ Nurse(s)/Doctor(s) _____

Gestational age _____ Weight/height _____

Oxygen needs _____ Apnea/brady spells _____

Feeding volume _____ Blood gas _____

Daily plan (tests/scans/procedures)

```



```

Vistors: _____

Today at a glance/milestones

How was the day

1   2   3   4   5   (circle one)

```



```

Today I am GRATEFUL for: _____

_____

_____

"Sometimes the biggest act of **COURAGE** is a **SMALL ONE.**"

Author unknown

Photo/Keepsake

Our Journey

Day | 76

Our Journey

Day 76

Date _____ Nurse(s)/Doctor(s) _____

Gestational age _____ Weight/height _____

Oxygen needs _____ Apnea/brady spells _____

Feeding volume _____ Blood gas _____

Daily plan (tests/scans/procedures)

Vistors: _____

Today at a glance/milestones

How was the day

1   2   3   4   5   (circle one)

Today I am GRATEFUL for: _____

Our Journey

Day | 77

Our Journey

Day | 77

Date _____ Nurse(s)/Doctor(s) _____

Gestational age _____ Weight/height _____

Oxygen needs _____ Apnea/brady spells _____

Feeding volume _____ Blood gas _____

Daily plan (tests/scans/procedures)

[ ]

Vistors: _____

Today at a glance/milestones

How was the day

1   2   3   4   5   (circle one)

[ ]

Today I am GRATEFUL for: _____

_____

_____

Our Journey

Day 78

Our Journey

Day | 78

Date _____   Nurse(s)/Doctor(s) _____

Gestational age _____   Weight/height _____

Oxygen needs _____   Apnea/brady spells _____

Feeding volume _____   Blood gas _____

Daily plan (tests/scans/procedures)

Vistors: _____

Today at a glance/milestones

How was the day

1   2   3   4   5   (circle one)

Today I am GRATEFUL for: _____

Our Journey

Day 79

Our Journey   Day 79

Date _____   Nurse(s)/Doctor(s) _____

Gestational age _____   Weight/height _____

Oxygen needs _____   Apnea/brady spells _____

Feeding volume _____   Blood gas _____

Daily plan (tests/scans/procedures)

```
┌─────────────────────────────────────────────────┐
│                                                 │
│                                                 │
│                                                 │
│                                                 │
│                                                 │
└─────────────────────────────────────────────────┘
```

Vistors: _____

_____

How was the day

Today at a glance/milestones   1   2   3   4   5   (circle one)

```
┌─────────────────────────────────────────────────┐
│                                                 │
│                                                 │
│                                                 │
│                                                 │
│                                                 │
└─────────────────────────────────────────────────┘
```

Today I am GRATEFUL for: _____

_____

_____

Our Journey

Day 80

Our Journey

Day 80

Date _____ Nurse(s)/Doctor(s) _____

Gestational age _____ Weight/height _____

Oxygen needs _____ Apnea/brady spells _____

Feeding volume _____ Blood gas _____

Daily plan (tests/scans/procedures)

```



```

Vistors: _____

_____

How was the day

Today at a glance/milestones   1   2   3   4   5   (circle one)

```



```

Today I am GRATEFUL for: _____

_____

_____

"Sometimes the
LITTLEST
things take up the
most room in our heart."

Winnie the Pooh

Photo/Keepsake

Our Journey

Day 81

Our Journey   Day 81

Date _____   Nurse(s)/Doctor(s) _____

Gestational age _____   Weight/height _____

Oxygen needs _____   Apnea/brady spells _____

Feeding volume _____   Blood gas _____

Daily plan (tests/scans/procedures)

Vistors: _____

Today at a glance/milestones

How was the day
1   2   3   4   5   (circle one)

Today I am GRATEFUL for: _____

Our Journey

Day 82

Our Journey

Day 82

Date _____ Nurse(s)/Doctor(s) _____

Gestational age _____ Weight/height _____

Oxygen needs _____ Apnea/brady spells _____

Feeding volume _____ Blood gas _____

Daily plan (tests/scans/procedures)

| |
| |

Vistors: _____

_____

Today at a glance/milestones

How was the day

1   2   3   4   5   (circle one)

| |
| |

Today I am GRATEFUL for: _____

_____

_____

Our Journey

Day | 83

Our Journey

Day 83

Date _____ Nurse(s)/Doctor(s) _____

Gestational age _____ Weight/height _____

Oxygen needs _____ Apnea/brady spells _____

Feeding volume _____ Blood gas _____

Daily plan (tests/scans/procedures)

Vistors: _____

How was the day

Today at a glance/milestones

1   2   3   4   5   (circle one)

Today I am GRATEFUL for: _____

Our Journey

Day 84

Our Journey

Date _____ Nurse(s)/Doctor(s) _____

Gestational age _____ Weight/height _____

Oxygen needs _____ Apnea/brady spells _____

Feeding volume _____ Blood gas _____

Daily plan (tests/scans/procedures)

Vistors: _____

Today at a glance/milestones

How was the day

1   2   3   4   5   (circle one)

Today I am GRATEFUL for: _____

Our Journey

Day | 85

Our Journey

Day 85

Date _____ Nurse(s)/Doctor(s) _____

Gestational age _____ Weight/height _____

Oxygen needs _____ Apnea/brady spells _____

Feeding volume _____ Blood gas _____

Daily plan (tests/scans/procedures)

```
┌─────────────────────────────────────────────┐
│                                             │
│                                             │
│                                             │
│                                             │
│                                             │
└─────────────────────────────────────────────┘
```

Vistors: _____

_____

Today at a glance/milestones

How was the day

1   2   3   4   5   (circle one)

```
┌─────────────────────────────────────────────┐
│                                             │
│                                             │
│                                             │
│                                             │
│                                             │
└─────────────────────────────────────────────┘
```

Today I am GRATEFUL for: _____

_____

_____

"Sometimes the things we cannot change

END UP CHANGING US."

Author unknown

Photo/Keepsake

Our Journey

Day 86

Our Journey

Day | 86

Date _____ Nurse(s)/Doctor(s) _____

Gestational age _____ Weight/height _____

Oxygen needs _____ Apnea/brady spells _____

Feeding volume _____ Blood gas _____

Daily plan (tests/scans/procedures)

```

```

Vistors: _____

Today at a glance/milestones

How was the day

1   2   3   4   5   (circle one)

```

```

Today I am GRATEFUL for: _____

_____

_____

Our Journey

Day 87

Our Journey   Day   87

Date _____   Nurse(s)/Doctor(s) _____

Gestational age _____   Weight/height _____

Oxygen needs _____   Apnea/brady spells _____

Feeding volume _____   Blood gas _____

Daily plan (tests/scans/procedures)

Vistors: _____

_____

Today at a glance/milestones

How was the day

1   2   3   4   5   (circle one)

Today I am GRATEFUL for: _____

_____

_____

Our Journey

Day 88

Our Journey

Day 88

Date _____ Nurse(s)/Doctor(s) _____

Gestational age _____ Weight/height _____

Oxygen needs _____ Apnea/brady spells _____

Feeding volume _____ Blood gas _____

Daily plan (tests/scans/procedures)

```
[                                                            ]
```

Vistors: _____

How was the day

Today at a glance/milestones   1   2   3   4   5   (circle one)

```
[                                                            ]
```

Today I am GRATEFUL for: _____

_____

_____

Our Journey

Day 89

Our Journey   Day 89

Date _____   Nurse(s)/Doctor(s) _____

Gestational age _____   Weight/height _____

Oxygen needs _____   Apnea/brady spells _____

Feeding volume _____   Blood gas _____

Daily plan (tests/scans/procedures)

```



```

Vistors: _____

_____

                                         How was the day
Today at a glance/milestones   1   2   3   4   5   (circle one)

```



```

Today I am GRATEFUL for: _____

_____

_____

Our Journey

Day | 90

Our Journey

Day 90

Date _____ Nurse(s)/Doctor(s) _____

Gestational age _____ Weight/height _____

Oxygen needs _____ Apnea/brady spells _____

Feeding volume _____ Blood gas _____

Daily plan (tests/scans/procedures)

```
┌─────────────────────────────────────────┐
│                                         │
│                                         │
│                                         │
│                                         │
│                                         │
└─────────────────────────────────────────┘
```

Vistors: _____

Today at a glance/milestones

How was the day
1   2   3   4   5   (circle one)

```
┌─────────────────────────────────────────┐
│                                         │
│                                         │
│                                         │
│                                         │
│                                         │
└─────────────────────────────────────────┘
```

Today I am GRATEFUL for: _____

_____

_____

"Being a
PREEMIE MOM
means: finding new *milestones* to celebrate, even if it is a single gram gained."

Author unknown

Photo/Keepsake

Our Journey

Day 91

Our Journey   Day 91

Date _____   Nurse(s)/Doctor(s) _____

Gestational age _____   Weight/height _____

Oxygen needs _____   Apnea/brady spells _____

Feeding volume _____   Blood gas _____

Daily plan (tests/scans/procedures)

[ ]

Vistors: _____

How was the day

Today at a glance/milestones   1   2   3   4   5   (circle one)

[ ]

Today I am GRATEFUL for: _____

_____

_____

Our Journey

Day 92

Our Journey   Day 92

Date _____   Nurse(s)/Doctor(s) _____

Gestational age _____   Weight/height _____

Oxygen needs _____   Apnea/brady spells _____

Feeding volume _____   Blood gas _____

Daily plan (tests/scans/procedures)

Vistors: _____

Today at a glance/milestones

How was the day

1   2   3   4   5   (circle one)

Today I am GRATEFUL for: _____

Our Journey

Day 93

Our Journey

Day 93

Date _____ Nurse(s)/Doctor(s) _____

Gestational age _____ Weight/height _____

Oxygen needs _____ Apnea/brady spells _____

Feeding volume _____ Blood gas _____

Daily plan (tests/scans/procedures)

Vistors: _____

Today at a glance/milestones

How was the day

1   2   3   4   5   (circle one)

Today I am GRATEFUL for: _____

Our Journey

Day 94

Our Journey

Day 94

Date _____ Nurse(s)/Doctor(s) _____

Gestational age _____ Weight/height _____

Oxygen needs _____ Apnea/brady spells _____

Feeding volume _____ Blood gas _____

Daily plan (tests/scans/procedures)

```



```

Vistors: _____
_____

How was the day

Today at a glance/milestones   1   2   3   4   5   (circle one)

```



```

Today I am GRATEFUL for: _____
_____
_____

Our Journey

Day 95

Our Journey

Date _____ Nurse(s)/Doctor(s) _____

Gestational age _____ Weight/height _____

Oxygen needs _____ Apnea/brady spells _____

Feeding volume _____ Blood gas _____

Daily plan (tests/scans/procedures)

```

```

Vistors: _____

Today at a glance/milestones

How was the day
1   2   3   4   5   (circle one)

```

```

Today I am GRATEFUL for: _____

_____

_____

Look for something **POSITIVE** in every day, even if some days you have to look a little harder."

Author Unknown

Photo/Keepsake

Our Journey

Day **96**

Our Journey   Day 96

Date _____   Nurse(s)/Doctor(s) _____

Gestational age _____   Weight/height _____

Oxygen needs _____   Apnea/brady spells _____

Feeding volume _____   Blood gas _____

Daily plan (tests/scans/procedures)

```
┌─────────────────────────────────────────────────────────┐
│                                                           │
│                                                           │
│                                                           │
│                                                           │
│                                                           │
└─────────────────────────────────────────────────────────┘
```

Vistors: _____
_____

Today at a glance/milestones

How was the day
1   2   3   4   5   (circle one)

```
┌─────────────────────────────────────────────────────────┐
│                                                           │
│                                                           │
│                                                           │
│                                                           │
│                                                           │
└─────────────────────────────────────────────────────────┘
```

Today I am GRATEFUL for: _____
_____
_____

Our Journey

Day 97

Our Journey

Day 97

Date _____ Nurse(s)/Doctor(s) _____

Gestational age _____ Weight/height _____

Oxygen needs _____ Apnea/brady spells _____

Feeding volume _____ Blood gas _____

Daily plan (tests/scans/procedures)

Vistors: _____

How was the day

Today at a glance/milestones   1   2   3   4   5   (circle one)

Today I am GRATEFUL for: _____

Our Journey

Day 98

Our Journey

Day 98

Date _____ Nurse(s)/Doctor(s) _____

Gestational age _____ Weight/height _____

Oxygen needs _____ Apnea/brady spells _____

Feeding volume _____ Blood gas _____

Daily plan (tests/scans/procedures)

```



```

Vistors: _____

_____

Today at a glance/milestones

How was the day

1   2   3   4   5   (circle one)

```



```

Today I am GRATEFUL for: _____

_____

_____

Our Journey

Day 99

Our Journey

Date _____ Nurse(s)/Doctor(s) _____

Gestational age _____ Weight/height _____

Oxygen needs _____ Apnea/brady spells _____

Feeding volume _____ Blood gas _____

Daily plan (tests/scans/procedures)

```
┌─────────────────────────────────────────────┐
│                                               │
│                                               │
│                                               │
│                                               │
│                                               │
└─────────────────────────────────────────────┘
```

Vistors: _____

_____

How was the day

Today at a glance/milestones   1   2   3   4   5   (circle one)

```
┌─────────────────────────────────────────────┐
│                                               │
│                                               │
│                                               │
│                                               │
│                                               │
└─────────────────────────────────────────────┘
```

Today I am GRATEFUL for: _____

_____

_____

Our Journey

Day | **100**

_____

_____

_____

_____

_____

_____

_____

_____

_____

_____

_____

_____

_____

_____

_____

_____

_____

_____

_____

_____

_____

_____

_____

Our Journey

Day 100

Date _____ Nurse(s)/Doctor(s) _____

Gestational age _____ Weight/height _____

Oxygen needs _____ Apnea/brady spells _____

Feeding volume _____ Blood gas _____

Daily plan (tests/scans/procedures)

```
```

Vistors: _____
_____

Today at a glance/milestones

How was the day

1   2   3   4   5   (circle one)

```
```

Today I am GRATEFUL for: _____
_____
_____

"You are a true warrior; every day is a

PRECIOUS MILESTONE!"

Alvaretta Roberts

Photo/Keepsake

MILESTONES
Beyond the NICU

TRACY MAY

MILESTONES
Beyond the NICU

MILESTONES
Beyond the NICU

TRACY MAY

MILESTONES
Beyond the NICU

MILESTONES
Beyond the NICU

TRACY MAY

MILESTONES
Beyond the NICU

MILESTONES
Beyond the NICU

TRACY MAY

MILESTONES
Beyond the NICU

MILESTONES
Beyond the NICU

TRACY MAY

MILESTONES
Beyond the NICU

MILESTONES
Beyond the NICU

TRACY MAY

MILESTONES
Beyond the NICU

MILESTONES
Beyond the NICU

TRACY MAY

MILESTONES
Beyond the NICU

MILESTONES
Beyond the NICU

TRACY MAY

MILESTONES
Beyond the NICU

MILESTONES
Beyond the NICU

TRACY MAY

MILESTONES
Beyond the NICU

MILESTONES
Beyond the NICU

TRACY MAY

MILESTONES
Beyond the NICU